Acoustic Classics

Arranged for Piano, Voice & Guitar

Let the River Run

Hal Leonard Europe
Distributed by Music Sales

Order No. HLE90000011
ISBN 0-7119-6303-7

Exclusive Distributors:
Music Sales Limited
8/9 Frith Street, London W1V 5TZ, England.
Music Sales Pty Limited
120 Rothschild Avenue, Rosebery, NSW 2018, Australia.

Printed in the USA

Your Guarantee of Quality
As publishers, we strive to produce every book to the
highest commercial standards.
This book has been carefully designed to minimise awkward
page turns and to make playing from it a real pleasure.
Throughout, the printing and binding have been planned to ensure a sturdy,
attractive publication which should give years of enjoyment.
If your copy fails to meet our high standards, please inform
us and we will gladly replace it.

Music Sales' complete catalogue describes thousands of titles and is
available in full colour sections by subject, direct from Music Sales Limited.
Please state your areas of interest and send a cheque/postal order for £1.50 for postage to:
Music Sales Limited, Newmarket Road, Bury St. Edmunds, Suffolk IP33 3YB.

Visit the Internet Music Shop at
http://www.musicsales.co.uk

AMERICAN PIE

Words and Music by
DON McLEAN

MCA music publishing

But Feb-ru-ar-y made me shiv-er with ev-'ry pa-per I'd de-liv-er.

Bad news on the door-step I could-n't take one more step I

can't re-mem-ber if I cried when I read a-bout __ his wid-owed bride,

Some-thing touched me deep in-side _____ the day the mu-sic died. _____

Additional Lyrics

2. Now for ten years we've been on our own,
   And moss grows fat on a rollin' stone
   But that's not how it used to be
   When the jester sang for the king and queen
   In a coat he borrowed from James Dean
   And a voice that came from you and me
   Oh and while the king was looking down,
   The jester stole his thorny crown
   The courtroom was adjourned,
   No verdict was returned
   And while Lenin read a book on Marx
   The quartet practiced in the park
   And we sang dirges in the dark
   The day the music died
   We were singin'... bye-bye... etc.

3. Helter-skelter in the summer swelter
   The birds flew off with a fallout shelter
   Eight miles high and fallin' fast,
   it landed foul on the grass
   The players tried for a forward pass,
   With the jester on the sidelines in a cast
   Now the half-time air was sweet perfume
   While the sergeants played a marching tune
   We all got up to dance
   But we never got the chance
   'Cause the players tried to take the field,
   The marching band refused to yield
   Do you recall what was revealed
   The day the music died
   We started singin'... bye-bye... etc.

4. And there we were all in one place,
   A generation lost in space
   With no time left to start again
   So come on, Jack be nimble, Jack be quick,
   Jack Flash sat on a candlestick
   'Cause fire is the devil's only friend
   And as I watched him on the stage
   My hands were clenched in fists of rage
   No angel born in hell
   Could break that Satan's spell
   And as the flames climbed high into the night
   To light the sacrificial rite
   I saw Satan laughing with delight
   The day the music died
   He was singin'... bye-bye... etc.

ANNIE'S SONG

Words and Music by
JOHN DENVER

Moderately

You fill up my sens - es _____

_____ like a night in a for - est, _____ like the

moun - tains in spring - time, _____ like a walk in the

AND I LOVE YOU SO

Words and Music by
DON McLEAN

MCA music publishing

BRIDGE OVER TROUBLED WATER

Words and Music by
PAUL SIMON

I will lay me down.

Rubato

When you're

Trou-bled Wa-ter I will lay me down.

25

BLACKBIRD

Words and Music by JOHN LENNON
and PAUL McCARTNEY

BLOWIN' IN THE WIND

Words and Music by
BOB DYLAN

CALIFORNIA DREAMIN'

Words and Music by JOHN PHILLIPS
and MICHELLE PHILLIPS

CASTLES IN THE AIR

Words and Music by
DON McLEAN

MCA music publishing

38

COME MONDAY

Words and Music by
JIMMY BUFFETT

And, hon-ey, I did-n't know__ that I'd be miss-in' you so.__
And, dar-lin', it's I love you so,__ that's the rea-son I just__ let you go.__ } Come
Cal - i - for -nia has worn me quite thin,__ I just can't wait to see__ you a - gain.__

gradual cresc.

mf

Mon-day_____ it -'ll be all right,__ Come Mon-day I'll be hold - in' you tight. I spent

four lone -ly days in a brown L. A. haze__ and I just want you back by my side.

1.   2.   I can't help it, hon-ey,__

COME SATURDAY MORNING
(Saturday Morning)
from the Paramount Picture THE STERILE CUCKOO

Words by DORY PREVIN
Music by FRED KARLIN

44

EL CONDOR PASA
(If I Could)

English Lyric by PAUL SIMON
Musical arramgement by JORGE MILCHBERG and DANIEL ROBLES

THE FIRST TIME EVER I SAW YOUR FACE

Words and Music by
EWAN MacCOLL

FREE BIRD

Words and Music by ALLEN COLLINS
and RONNIE VAN ZANT

HERE COMES THE SUN

Words and Music by
GEORGE HARRISON

Sun, sun, sun, here it comes.

D.S. al Coda

HOMEWARD BOUND

Words and Music by
PAUL SIMON

I WILL

Words and Music by JOHN LENNON
and PAUL McCARTNEY

I'LL FOLLOW THE SUN

Words and Music by JOHN LENNON
and PAUL McCARTNEY

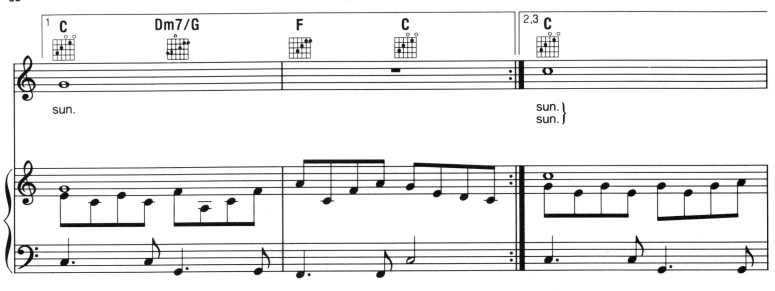

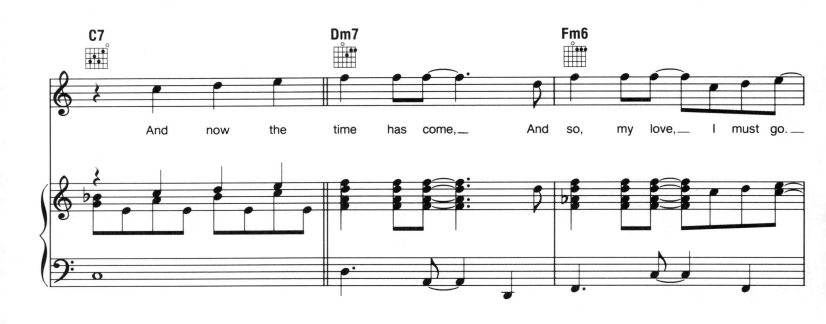

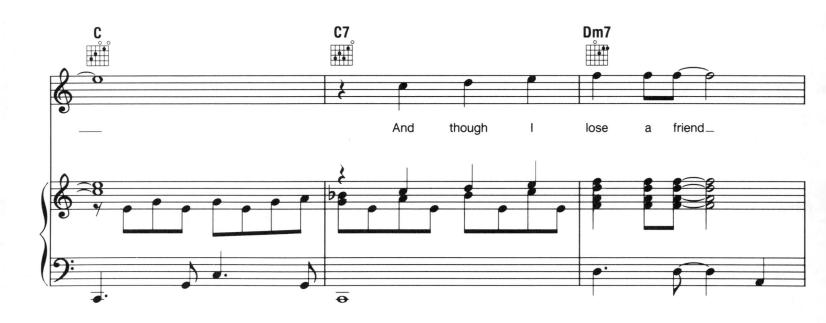

I'VE JUST SEEN A FACE

Words and Music by JOHN LENNON
and PAUL McCARTNEY

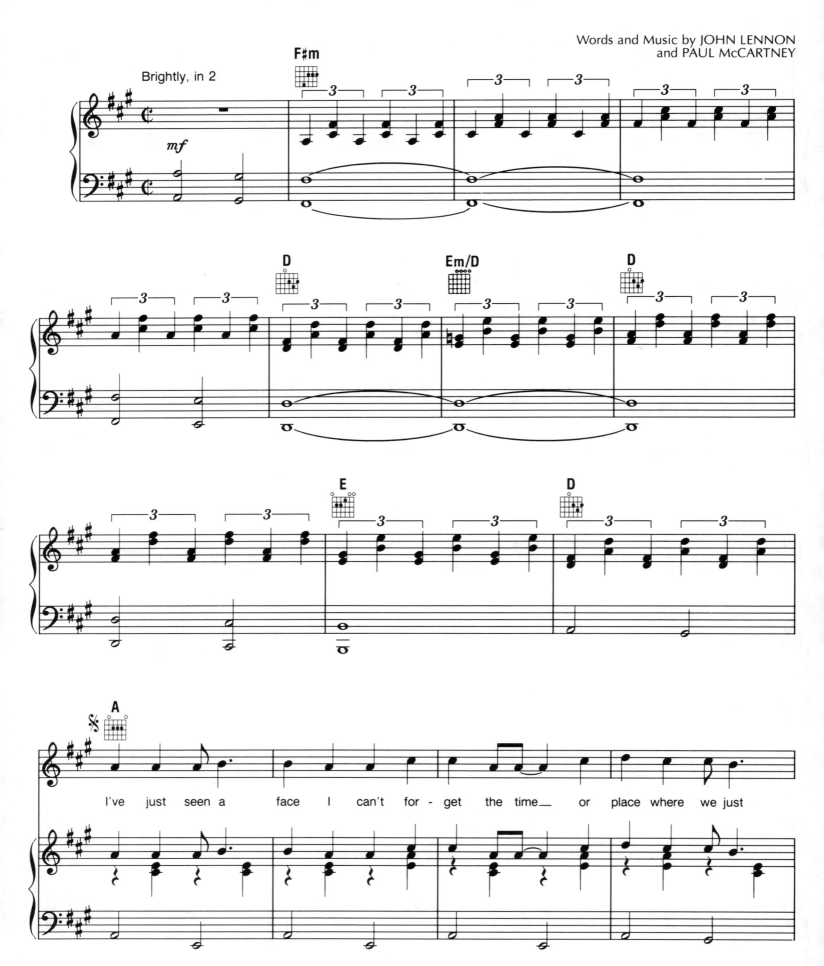

I've just seen a face I can't for - get the time___ or place where we just

IF I HAD A HAMMER
(The Hammer Song)

Words and Music by LEE HAYS
and PETE SEEGER

IMAGINE

Words and Music by
JOHN LENNON

LEAVING ON A JET PLANE

Words and Music by
JOHN DENVER

LOVE IS ALL AROUND
Featured on the Motion Picture Soundtrack FOUR WEDDINGS AND A FUNERAL

Words and Music by
REG PRESLEY

MY SWEET LADY

Words and Music by
JOHN DENVER

ROCKY RACCOON

Moderately, in two (♩ = 1 beat)

Words and Music by JOHN LENNON
and PAUL McCARTNEY

help with good Rock - y's re - vi - val.

Barrelhouse style (♪♪ played as ♪ ♪)

NORWEGIAN WOOD
(This Bird Has Flown)

Words and Music by JOHN LENNON
and PAUL McCARTNEY

THE SOUND OF SILENCE

Words and Music by
PAUL SIMON

STILL CRAZY AFTER ALL THESE YEARS

Words and Music by
PAUL SIMON

TURN! TURN! TURN!
(To Everything There Is a Season)

Words from the Book of Ecclesiastes
Adaptation and Music by PETE SEEGER

UNTIL IT'S TIME FOR YOU TO GO

Words and Music by
BUFFY SAINTE-MARIE

Slow Waltz

VINCENT
(Starry Starry Night)

Words and Music by
DON McLEAN

MCA music publishing

121

WHERE HAVE ALL THE FLOWERS GONE?

Words & Music by PETE SEEGER

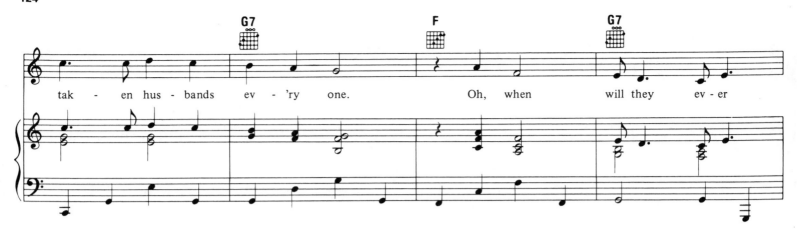

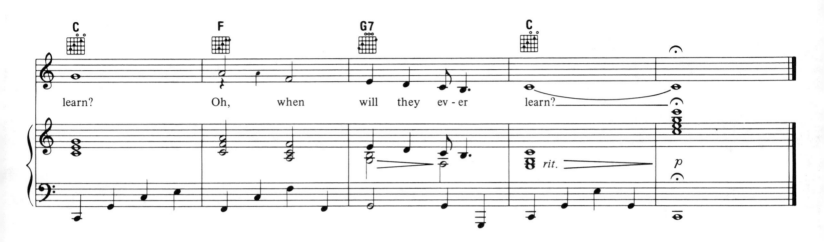

3. Where have all the young men gone? Long time passing.
Where have all the young men gone? Long time ago.
Where have all the young men gone?
They're all in uniform.
Oh, when will they ever learn?
Oh, when will they ever learn?

4. Where have all the soldiers gone? Long time passing.
Where have all the soldiers gone? Long time ago.
Where have all the soldiers gone?
They've gone to graveyards, every one.
Oh, when will they ever learn?
Oh, when will they ever learn?

5. Where have all the graveyards gone? Long time passing.
Where have all the graveyards gone? Long time ago.
Where have all the graveyards gone?
They're covered with flowers, every one.
Oh, when will they ever learn?
Oh, when will they ever learn?

6. Where Have All The Flowers Gone? Long time passing.
Where Have All The Flowers Gone? Long time ago.
Where Have All The Flowers Gone?
Young girls picked them, every one.
Oh, when will they ever learn?
Oh, when will they ever learn?

YOUR SONG

Slow, but with a beat

Words and Music by ELTON JOHN and BERNIE TAUPIN

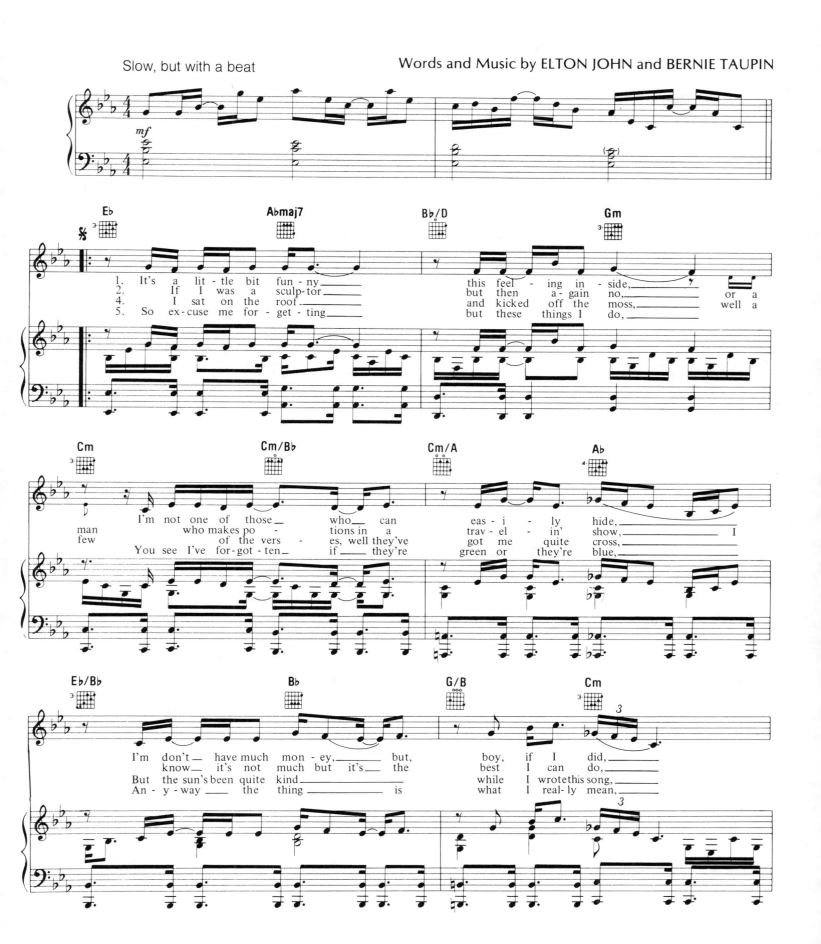